STAR QUEST

An incredible voyage into the unknown

Steven Caldwell

CRESCENT
New York

Contents

Page

Visitor from beyond 4

Voyage into the unknown 10

The first encounter 16

Planet of death 26

The warrior queen 34

The Phalan empire 42

The tables turn 48

Flight to Terra 56

Epilogue 62

Illustration credits
Jim Burns, *pages 8/9, 18/19 & 41*; Peter Elson, *pages 5, 6/7, 12/13, 15, 22/23, 28/29, 35, 43, 44/45, 46/47, 49 & 59*; Bob Fowkes, *pages 36/37*; Fred Gambino, *title page & pages 11 & 57*; Colin Hay, *pages 21, 31, 32/33 & 38/39*; Robin Hiddon, *front cover*; David Jackson, *pages 24/25 & 64*; Bob Layzell, *page 27*; Chris Moore, *pages 52/53, 54/55 & 60/61*; Cesare Reggiani, *page 17*; Tony Roberts, *pages 50/51 & 62/63*.

Introduction

By the twenty-third century, the Galactic Federation had grown to occupy a volume almost 500 light years in diameter. Within its sphere of influence were thousands of worlds and although most were uninhabited, a high proportion were the homes of indigenous species or were settled by colonists from elsewhere. Many more were scenes of industrial activity in the fields of mining or manufacturing, often by totally automated processes, and hundreds of thousands of vessels of every kind plied to and fro along the trade routes which led to every corner of the Federation.

During the very earliest period of the Federation's history, expansion outwards into the Galaxy had been comparatively rapid and uncontrolled, as both commercial interests and adventurous individuals pushed out into unknown space in search of wealth and open land. Death and disaster decimated the ranks of these intrepid explorers during this first rush for the stars until, gradually, the Federation began to impose controls and to institute a planned programme of expansion.

As a direct result, the rate of expansion slowed dramatically and greater emphasis was placed on consolidation and the efficient exploitation of existing resources.

Expansion did not, however, cease entirely and the survey ships sponsored by the authorities continued to probe into the darkness beyond the official frontiers charting and gathering data on the worlds they encountered. In addition, the newly settled planets on the Federal Perimeter were becoming more securely established, creating further opportunities for trade and shipping.

Despite this industrious spiral of development and activity, the authorities were constantly aware that although the Federation had already grown larger than could have been imagined just 200 or 300 Earth-years earlier, it nevertheless represented only a minute area of the Galaxy. Given the number of inhabited worlds within its boundaries, it was certain that hundreds if not thousands of other intelligent forms of life must lie among the countless stars beyond. It was just a matter of time before we encountered a species or group of species as technologically advanced as those of the Federation, and quite possibly more so. The obvious advantage of searching out and identifying any such species before they stumbled on the Federation, however, was outweighed by the economic difficulty of searching through a gigantic haystack for very small needles that might not even exist. It certainly could not be justified without there being any evidence of alien species.

That evidence came to light when a Security Patrol ship on a routine mission among the Perimeter planets stumbled on the existence of an alien ship that had not originated from within the Federation. This brief encounter heralded the start of one of the most ambitious journeys of exploration ever undertaken. The voyage of the Venturer stands out as one of the most remarkable episodes in the annals of space travel. The courage of its dedicated crew in the face of the uncertainty of the mission's outcome is still more remarkable when each man knew at the outset of the voyage that due to the relative time effects of prolonged hyperspace travel, any of them returning home would have aged only days for each year of real time. Those they had left behind would be long dead and once familiar worlds would have changed almost beyond recognition.

Star Quest, then, is their story.

CHAPTER ONE

Visitor from beyond

LOG POINT: Retrospective summary.
DUTY OFFICER: Commander Mor Mikiss.
DRIVE MODE: Not applicable.
DRIVE STATUS: Pre-flight readiness.
SYSTEMS STATUS: Pre-flight readiness.
PERSONNEL STATUS: Undergoing advanced training routine as to Directive No. SFSM 447.

From beyond the edge of known space came this strange visitor to the Galactic Federation. Where it was from and what would happen now that it knew we existed were questions that could no longer remain unanswered..

Far out among the distant stars of the Perimeter, in the early years of the 23rd century, Scoutships and Pathfinders of the Galactic Federation were patrolling the boundaries of known space. The complex web of interstellar trade had not yet extended this far and few craft ventured among the charted, but almost unknown planets that lay scattered in the lonely frontier region. Apart from the stained and battered hulls of deep space prospectors looking for the rainbow's end, the only vessels to navigate those desolate reaches were the survey ships and mobile laboratories of the Federal Research Institute.

The alien ship from Arko.

A few planets supported small colonial settlements struggling to gain a foothold in alien worlds, but they were not secure enough to participate in trade with the systems nearer the hub of the Federation. Their only regular contact was through the patrol craft that called at intervals to check on their charges. The light cruiser *Arko* was on just such a mission when its detector gear registered a contact that was to result in one of the most extraordinary voyages in the history of space travel.

Shortly after a change of watch the navigation console started calculating the course, speed and mass of an object moving through space less than a million miles away. The duty officer duly logged the event and settled back into his seat: interstellar space contains numerous particles of free-moving matter ranging from particles of dust to massive asteroids. They do, however, travel in straight lines unless captured by a gravitational field, so when the computers detected a change of course, the officer was alerted. No ships had requested clearance for this region, so with visions of smugglers or illegal ore miners and a chance to break

the endless routine of a long distance flight, he raised the alarm. But by the time the crew were on station, the data being gathered by the detector gear described a ship that failed to match any type in its memory, and the captain ordered a combat alert. As they closed on an intercepting course he keyed in the Visiscan to full magnification. As the image steadied, he let out an involuntary gasp of surprise.

Centered on the screen was one of the strangest vessels he had seen in all his years of service. As he jabbed the Image Record control, the massive, bowed shape of the alien vessel slowed and turned like some gigantic insect. He reduced speed slightly and with a nod to his signals officer, ordered the transmission of the standard Galactic identification request, but there was no response to that or to any of the codes used by individual species within the Federation. The stern of the huge, angular ship was obviously a drive unit of some kind, but its rounded shape did not conform to any type known among the worlds of the Galactic Federation.

They were within a few miles of the alien form, when

the globe-like stern began to glow and seconds later, the ship accelerated at an incalculable speed and vanished into the background of stars. Their mission to the distant settlers forgotten, the patrol ship came about and returned to base in maximum warp.

Within minutes of the message reaching Security Headquarters on Earth all local stations were instructed to check the whereabouts of any registered vessel that might fit the description of the strange craft and be capable of deep-space operation, but within two days all possible craft had been accounted for. The only explanation was that within reach of us, somewhere in the darkness beyond the Perimeter lay a race of intelligent beings at least as advanced technologically as ourselves. The question of whether they had known of our existence

After sighting the alien craft, the patrol ship Arko *headed back to base under maximum power to break the news that an unknown advanced civilisation must lie somewhere in the darkness beyond the Perimeter.*

beforehand, or whether it had been a chance encounter and what their intentions might be, were obviously matters of the utmost importance. A conference at the highest level was called.

During the following days, a succession of shuttles brought the representatives of every world within the Federation to the tall, slender tower of Security Headquarters which rose from an atoll in Earth's Pacific Ocean. The significance of the stranger's arrival and the importance of determining its place of origin was unanimously agreed almost at once,

The constellation Canis Major.

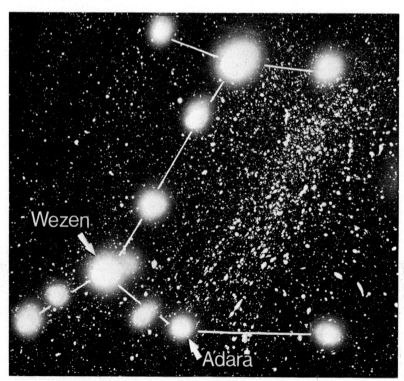

Wezen

Adara

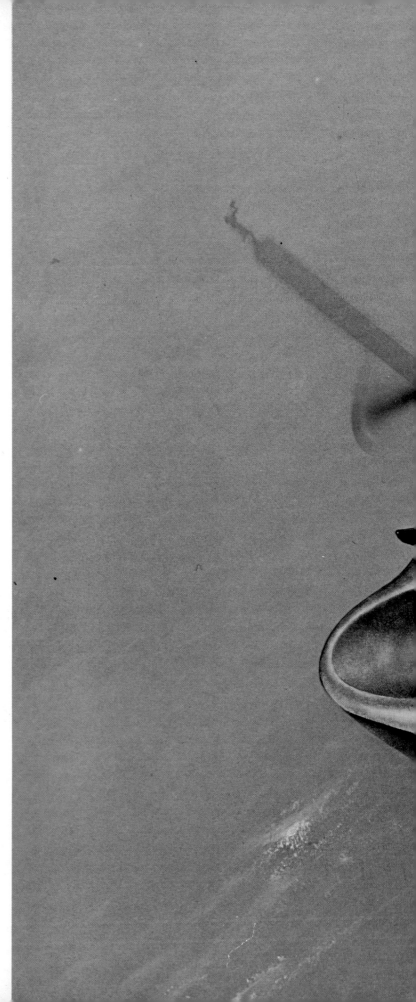

*After the news of the alien
ship reached the Federation,
representatives from every
member planet began
arriving at Security
Headquarters to decide what
course of action to take.*

but the question of what
course of action to take was
debated for many long hours.

Finally a decision was
reached. The only way to
discover where such a ship
might come from was to
search far beyond the Perimeter Worlds. A hand-
picked crew had to be found
who were willing to embark
on a voyage deep into un-
known space from which
they might never return. Although travelling at many
times the speed of light it
was probable that by the time
they returned everything that
was familiar to them in normal
space/time would have vanished or altered beyond
recognition.

The task of finding such a
team began, and the com-
puters in every branch of the
service churned through file
after file until a list of possible
members was compiled for
the High Command to peruse.
Personnel from every corner
of the Federation found themselves mysteriously summ-
oned to undergo exhaustive
examinations without explanation until a handful of men
and women were brought
together and informed of
the proposed voyage and
its objectives. From those
who volunteered was drawn
the small band who would be
trained to the highest possible degree, and would have
nothing to rely on but their
own initiative and expertise
in the endless vacuum far
from their fellow beings.

CHAPTER TWO

Voyage into the unknown

LOG POINT: Pre-flight schedule point 0326.
DUTY OFFICER: Commander Mor Mikiss.
DRIVE STATUS: A1. Operational readiness.
SYSTEMS STATUS: A1. Operational readiness.
PERSONNEL STATUS: Operational readiness.
Morale high.

By the time the list of volunteers who had successfully completed the rigorous selection programme had been drawn up, all of them knew the general nature of the task they were being asked to perform, and each looked forward to the initial briefing with a mixture of excitement and uncertainty. The severity of the tests imposed upon them had made it clear that the survivors would be those who possessed qualities or abilities of the highest order, and it was with some trepidation that twelve men and women answered the summons to the main briefing room situated deep in Security Headquarters.

As they assembled in the dimly lit chamber, each recognized many of the other faces around the central arena, before a door hissed open to admit a number of the most senior officers in the Federation. Among them stood the tall, solid figure of Mor Mikiss, one of the legendary figures of the Space Patrol whose reputation as an operational officer was unequalled throughout the Federation. As the room fell silent and the volunteers took their seats, they could feel the cool gaze of their commander-to-be as it travelled slowly over the row of expectant faces. Then all

eyes were turned upon the Director General of the Galactic Security Command as he rose to welcome them and to introduce them to each other by giving a brief resumé of each person's qualifications and describing the role intended for them in the new team.

As he talked, the huge Vidscreen behind him displayed the faces and a brief synopsis of the individual members:

Richard Pontine, Chief Navigations Officer, a specialist in Deep Space orientation and Hyperspace spectrum analysis.
Dor Hewett, Systems Engineer, and computer expert who designed the Intuitive Input System.
Dick Frost, Drive Engineer who developed the FASTA (Field Attenuating Space/ Time Accelerator) System for boosting Hyperdrive effect, now standard on most Federal ships.
Graham Frankeve, Astro Physicist and authority on parallel space.
Mas Rahzell, Communications Officer, also an expert on sub-space code referencing.
Lorac Reab, Nutritionist and Hydroponics expert who isolated the protein-rich compound known as Hydroxysiritein B.

Nibor Max, Environmental Biologist, widely known for his work among the Perimeter Worlds.
Mary Mogab, Psychologist specializing in closed environment stress.
Jancis Joh, Cultural Psychologist and Anthropologist with considerable experience of working among alien species.
Tik Rednop, Linguistics authority largely responsible for developing interpretive programmes for multi-function computers.
Coral Dee, Practical Strategist and Function Analyst.
Art West, Armaments Officer and Tactician seconded from the Galactic Security Force, Field Action Training Center.

The Director General then described the alien contact made by the *Arko* and the need to establish the origins of the strange craft. There was no need to state the difficulties and dangers of a mission into the unknown reaches beyond the furthest boundaries of the Federation

The legendary Commander Mor Mikiss, one of the most experienced and respected operational officers in the Security Service was the natural choice as leader of the unique team.
Overleaf
After weeks of extensive training and preparation, the day finally arrived when the charter shuttles carried the crew to the Way Station where they were to board the ship for the start of the epic voyage.

as they could be imagined only too well by the seasoned spacers assembled there. Having outlined the objective of the mission, the Director General introduced the Technical officer responsible for equipping the team, who proceeded to brief them on the many specialized items of hardware with which they would be supplied. The room darkened and he stepped over to the control console. A few seconds later, the holographic image of a Venturer Class battleship in miniature glowed in the center of the floor as he went on to explain the choice of vessel and its specifications. Although somewhat outdated in many respects, it was, nevertheless, renowned for its ruggedness and durability and several examples were still in front-line service.

There would have to be a number of modifications made to make it suitable for prolonged deep-space operation, but the basic construction was as sound as any of the more recent ships, and its military specifications allowed an extra margin of safety. After a period of discussion, the group broke up for detailed briefings in their separate responsibilities, a pattern which was to last

for several days, before they were taken to the dockyard where the vessel was undergoing her refit. The next few weeks were an endless succession of training and familiarization sessions until every member of the crew was almost at the point of exhaustion and the whole project had started to acquire an air of unreality.

Finally the Venturer was ready for her trials and the crew boarded for the first of many test runs out towards the Perimeter. Inevitably there were many small difficulties to overcome, but gradually each individual in the team settled into his or her role and the thirteen very different personalities began to merge together into a single unit. By now there was a growing feeling of impatience. The training sessions started to become tedious and repetitive as they awaited a definite date for the start of the voyage. As there was still some work to be done on the Venturer after the extensive trials, and the training programme had come to an end, leave was given to the team to allow them to relax and make their farewells before being ferried out to the orbital Way-Station where the ship was finally

The Venturer, distinctive in its scarlet and black livery, moves out under military escort before entering hyperspace for the first leg of its journey into the unknown.

being prepared for space.

Three weeks later, Earth Time, each crew member received the call to assemble at the Security Headquarters where the last medical checks were made, followed by the farewell exchanges with the staff of the training center. The Director General and other senior officials of the Federation were already at the Station for the final departure, and the thirteen men and women who might be spending the rest of their lives together, boarded the charter shuttles for the short ride to where the Venturer hung alongside the wheel-like Station.

The speeches were brief and informal with none of the publicity that such a dramatic enterprise might normally have attracted, and the crew were soon aboard the huge, crimson ship, running through the pre-flight routines. When all the status reports had been received by Commander Mikiss, the drive units were brought on line as the traditional Bon Voyage signal was beamed out from the Station. An escort of Security interceptors accompanied the Venturer as she moved out to take up position for Warp entry. The crew glanced at the blue-green globe of Earth once more before the view winked out as they entered hyperspace. The greatest adventure in the history of Man had begun.

A Venturer Class battleship was chosen for the mission.

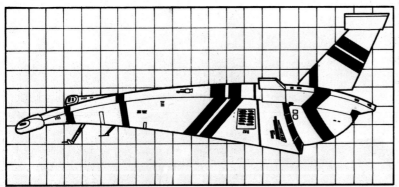

CHAPTER THREE

The first encounter

LOG POINT: Ref. 1272. Proximity Epsilon Canis Majoris.
DUTY OFFICER: CommOff. Mas Rahzell.
DRIVE MODE: Primary.
DRIVE STATUS: A1.
SYSTEMS STATUS: A1. Minor variances in secondary generator. Output being monitored.
PERSONNEL STATUS: Morale good.

The transition to Warp Mode was scarcely noticeable to the crew of the Venturer as they prepared for the long sleep of cryogenic stasis while the ship hurtled out towards the Perimeter Worlds which marked the boundary of known space. They would remain frozen for the first part of the voyage until they had passed the limit already reached by unmanned probes, or until woken by the automatic systems guiding the craft through the kaleidoscope of sub-space.

Weeks later by real time, seconds later by the crew's body time, the Venturer identified itself to the last Federal beacon before plunging into the darkness where no human had ever been before. Outside the hull, the extraordinary light and colour of hyperspace shimmered and danced disturbingly. Inside, in direct contrast, the only sound was the almost inaudible hum of the monitors and environment systems protecting the crew as they lay, suspended in time in their "sleep-tanks". None of them knew how long it would be before they were released from the dreamless night of stasis, or what they would find when they awoke and

stepped from their "tanks" into the empty and echoing control rooms.

When the mysterious alien ship had vanished from the sight of Arko's crew it had been heading in the direction of Canis Major. The Venturer was on course for Gamma Canis Majoris which was the nearest star, at 325 light years from Earth, outside the Federation's boundaries. As it approached the white helium star, lights came on in the empty corridors and control rooms, the temperature climbed and air hissed from the vents as the ship began to come back to life. The crew stirred in their tanks as their bodies responded to the urg-

Adara's three inner planets.

ings of the revitalizer circuits and before long they were gathering in the main control room or checking the readings from the central console, as the ship started to record and analyse initial data on the system ahead. Mor Mikiss and his ship's function officers prepared for the transfer into real space, and a short while later the Venturer winked into existence and hung motionless with the brilliant light of Gamma Canis Majoris centered in the viewscreens. All personnel settled into the routine of programming and directing the intricate equipment to conduct a preliminary sweep of the star's vicinity, but it soon became apparent that no non-luminous bodies attended the solitary sun, and a meeting was held to decide their next move in the search for the origins of the Federation's strange visitor.

The next star outwards was Epsilon Canis Majoris, or Adara, which lies at 470 light years from Earth and a

The three man team from the Venturer streaked downwards to make the first contact with the medieval inhabitants of Adara III.
Overleaf
While on a lone study trip to one of the outlying villages, Doctor Jancis Joh was seized by raiders from one of the grim warrior tribes of the north, and was carried away from her colleagues along the extraordinary cableways which crisscrossed the planet's surface.

course was set accordingly. The crew decided not to re-enter freeze for the comparatively short journey and settled down to while away the weeks ahead. The technicians had provided on board as many facilities as any of the luxurious liners which travelled among the worlds of the Federation and as the distance was less than a trip from Earth to one of the Perimeter Worlds, the journey passed easily enough.

Most of the crew were asleep when the scanners registered the proximity of the B1 supergiant. As they stumbled onto the control deck, Mor Mikiss was already conducting the transfer from sub-space. Although they were nearly 3000 million miles away, the brilliant white sphere filled the scanner screens as they sat down at their various consoles to start the sweep. They found that the Venturer had already entered a planetary system, and was lying inside the orbit of the furthermost of five satellites. They began the laborious task of studying the individual worlds and

soon established that only one was capable of supporting life in any form. The Venturer edged in slowly towards the small planet that swung in the middle of the five orbiting companions as the scanners analysed mass, spectrum and albedo and formulated a profile of the world below.

Small settlements and areas of cultivation were soon identified but infra-red readings failed to isolate any area that might suggest an industrial technology and there was certainly no sign that the inhabitants had developed a method of space travel. It was decided that Nibor Max, Jancis Joh and Tik Rednop would make a cautious attempt to make contact with the creatures below. They kitted up and climbed into one of the larger, armed shuttles and slid out of the lock for the descent to the largest visible settlement.

For the three envoys, the next week was spent making contact with the humanoid inhabitants of an almost medieval world. The many myths and legends of this simple,

Rearing out of the shallow, misty seas of the north lay the fortresses of the sinister raiders who frequently attacked the farming communities further inland.

agrarian society made their task easier, and they soon established that the alien ship could not have set out from here. But as they were preparing to leave, disaster struck. Jancis Joh failed to return from one of her frequent excursions into the small villages outside the main settlement. The others immediately set out for her original destination and discovered that she had been attacked by raiders from one of the mysterious and isolated northern tribal groups and carried off by these much feared warriors in one of the sail-cars that ran along the cableways which criss-crossed the surface of this world. The naive simplicity of the people had lulled the researchers into a false sense of security, and they had ceased to carry weapons of any kind, leaving Doctor Joh unprotected. It was going to be a problem to find her, as her locator beacon was discovered on the ground by the cableway's landing stage. Simple detective work would be the only method of tracing her whereabouts.

The first clue was provided by the villagers themselves, who identified the raiders as having come from a grim castle-city set in one of the mist-shrouded lakes far to the north. Nibor Max and Tik Rednop returned to the Venturer to discuss the situation. A full scale assault on the fortress was obviously impossible without endangering

The Venturer approaches Adara III.

As the crew of one of Venturer's landers tracked the ship carrying Dr Joh, a hideous shape burst from below the surface of the water to tower over the frail wooden vessel.

their colleague's life so the only chance was to head the kidnap party off before they could reach their destination. A skeleton crew was left aboard the Venturer while the others split into teams and descended to the planet surface in every available vehicle. There they each followed one of the cable-ways which served the northern regions until one team spotted a sailing vessel far below. It was heading out into the fogbanks of the polar seas where they knew from their earlier scans no landfall existed. It had to be sailing towards one of the sea-forts occupied by the raiders and was therefore worth closer investigation.

The team, Richard Pontine and Dor Hewett, manoeuvred their surface lander until it was directly over the ship but out of sight of the war-riors aboard, while they considered the problem of rescuing Doctor Joh without risking her life. Their craft was not equipped with the Berger Gravity Resist units fitted to craft specifically designed for frequent atmos-pheric operations so they were relying on conventional thrust drivers to stay aloft, and their fuel was rapidly running low. At that moment, their attention was caught by a massive dark shape just below the surface of the water, which was rapidly closing in on the wooden vessel. As they watched, the

two converged and the ship keeled over and lost way. Serpentine heads reared out of the sea to tower over the deck. Panic seemed to break out among the crew, and tiny figures scrambled away from the gigantic sea-creature while others tumbled over the side into the water. The great heads began striking at the frail hull, crushing and splintering the planking.

If Jancis Joh was aboard the wooden vessel her team-mates had to act now, and the lander plummeted towards the fearsome,writhing monster below as Pontine and Hewett frantically searched for the Doctor's figure amid the frenzied activity on the decks of the foundering ship. Suddenly, they spotted her in the water, swimming desperately away from the horrific scene as her captors struggled to save their vessel and drive the beast off with their spears and arrows. While Pontine swung the lander down towards the waves, Hewett delved into the storage lockers for some means of reaching Doctor Joh as they were unable to make a landing on water. A groundscooter nestled in one of the bays, and he dragged it bodily to an exit lock. Although intended for land travel, it was airtight and carried oxygen tanks and a pulsed atmosphere thrust unit. He shouted into the intercom and the lock door slid back. With a heave he toppled the little craft into the water where it disappeared before surging to the surface again. Doctor Joh swam towards it as the lander pulled away to keep the area clear of thrust. As she clambered into the scooter she

With its fuel reserves almost depleted, the lander lifted under maximum thrust with all the crew safely aboard.

opened the radio link and they decided to head for shore where they could meet.

Even before the grounding dust had settled, Doctor Joh was climbing into the lander, and they lifted again for the trip back to the Venturer. There was fifteen minutes of fuel left by the time they docked and shut the drives down.

The other searchers returned shortly afterwards and after greeting Doctor Joh they assembled for a conference on the main deck. Adara III could not have been the starting point of the alien ship, and a further destination would have to be decided. There would be ample time for rest once they were under way again. The long range scanners had registered the presence of a tiny G5 star within 130 light years distance which was not identified on the navigational data banks; they elected to head for it straight away.

A considerable mass of data had been accumulated during their brief stay in the Gamma Canis Majoris system which would occupy them for the next stage of the voyage. The excitement of the last few hours soon faded as they slipped yet again into sub-space and each member of the team began sifting through the accumulated information they had gathered. Meanwhile the small yellow star ahead grew hourly nearer until the proximity signal alerted the Commander for the next transfer into real space.

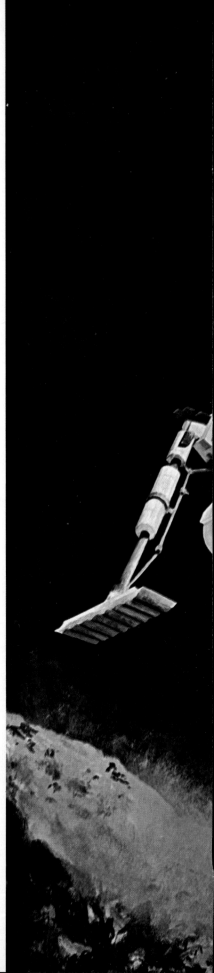

CHAPTER FOUR

Planet of death

LOG POINT: Ref. 1403. Proximity unidentified star coded VenX.
DUTY OFFICER: BiOff. Nibor Max.
DRIVE MODE: Warp.
DRIVE STATUS: A1.
SYSTEMS STATUS: A2. Secondary generator oscillating. Damaged feeder replaced.
PERSONNEL STATUS: Morale high.

As soon as they had emerged from warp, the scanners and data collectors began to accumulate information on the small G5 star ahead and its miniature system. A vast number of objects were in orbit around it, but only two could be described as planets. The rest were all asteroids of varying sizes, and one of the planets was no more than a ball of barren rock not much larger than Earth's moon. The other, however, appeared habitable, with an oxygen-rich atmosphere and a gravitational field only slightly stronger than that of Earth. There was an adequate water surface and the temperature range, although quite low, was within tolerance. The only curious factor was the presence of a considerable number of radiation "hot spots" scattered in an irregular pattern about the planet's surface.

After a comprehensive sweep of local space which revealed no sign of any artificial objects, the Venturer moved into a high static orbit and a close visual scrutiny of the surface began. It was immediately obvious that extensive artificial constructions existed on most of the bleak and sparsely vegetated land masses, but despite the industrial appearance of most of the complexes, there was no infra-red indication of localised heat generation to indicate concentrated activity. There was nevertheless something unsettling about the unattractive-looking planet, and Commander Mikiss cautiously accelerated the ship to conduct a global sweep pattern before making a closer approach. A few seconds later, the Signals Officer picked up a weak contact emanating from near the planet's terminator in a slightly lower orbit.

The crew stood to emergency stations as a pulsed sensor beam was "bounced" between the surface and the ionosphere. At intervals, the higher frequency burps would pass through the ionosphere to intersect with an orbital receiving beam in a blanket of spots around the orbital curve. An interruption in the pattern ahead of them indicated the presence of a metallic object just beneath the level of the receiving beam, and Art West, the Armaments Officer triggered the energy absorption screens and keyed the weapons control systems into the mainline computer.

Seconds later an alien ship appeared, glinting in the viewscreens and the Venturer drifted to a halt. Minutes passed without any acknowledgement from the ship that their presence had been detected, so a multi-frequency signal was beamed towards the silent vessel but with no effect. They tried laser signals with no greater success so the Venturer shifted into a parallel orbit and closed in. As they drew alongside, it became apparent that the craft had been drifting through space for a long time and was gradually spiralling down towards the planet's surface. Its sides were pitted and several minute scars indicated strikes by more substantial particles. That it was lifeless was indicated by a jagged gash near the bow where several fragments of debris floated in the vacuum.

Somehow this derelict sentinel only served to increase the feeling of tension that was beginning to pervade the Venturer, and the great ship altered course for a closer investigation of the silent planet. Despite the degree of technology demonstrated by the

As the survey team searched among the debris of an empty world, the awful truth of its fate gradually emerged. Over the entire surface lay the blasted and shattered ruins of an ancient and advanced species.
Overleaf
This solitary derelict was the first indication encountered of the desolation that lay below, as it endlessly circled the silent planet.

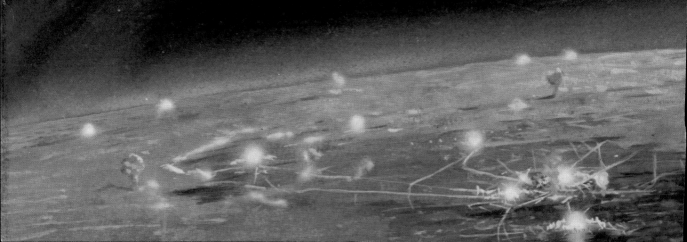

empty spacecraft, no signals could be detected from the levels beneath them as they approached the planet's cloudy atmospheric layers. Teams prepared to board two of the shuttles. They donned "hot suits" in view of the strange areas of high radiation that dotted the terrain, and slipped out of the launch bays with one craft maintaining a covering position for the other as the ground loomed up towards them.

Picking out one of the huge complexes, one shuttle dropped to ground level near the outskirts while the other held station overhead, but it was soon evident that such precautions were unnecessary. In every direction, the scanners presented an image of desolation and decay; scrubby undergrowth entangled with rusty, flaking metalwork and collapsing masonry. Nothing stirred in the eerie landscape except the dust from the shuttle's landing.

After checking the external environment and establishing that the radiation levels, although high, were within the tolerance of their suits, three of the crew stepped from the airlock onto the barren, sandy soil and made their way through scattered debris to the stained and rotting shape of a monorail vehicle that lay nearby. The absolute silence was unnerving, and after a fairly cursory examination of the derelict car and its surroundings, they returned to the shuttle with a feeling of relief.

Further checks confirmed that the entire area had been unoccupied for a very long time, so they decided to investigate one of the nearby areas of radioactivity. As they

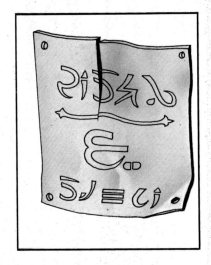

A fragment from the dead planet, found by the crew.

approached, the remains became more skeletal and fewer in number and the ground grew hard and glassy as though vitrified. Eventually, a huge, fused crater confirmed what the teams had already began to suspect, and they reported that the complex had been subject to a ferocious nuclear catastrophe in the distant past.

Further sorties to other parts of the shattered world confirmed that the entire planet had suffered a holocaust that could not have been accidental. The fall-out had blanketed and sterilized every corner of the globe. That there was any plant life at all was little short of a miracle and any attempt to find sentient life was abandoned.

The vital question was whether this had been the base of the Federation's elusive visitor. If so, it was unlikely that its occupants would pose a threat, as they would be merely bewildered refugees from an ancient, monumental war. Countering this supposition was the fact that the alien craft had displayed none of the signs of

age that would tally with the date of the disaster. Additionally, an internecine planetary conflict, however intense, was likely to leave some survivors, whereas there was every indication that a systematic destruction of all life had taken place. The aggressor must have come from elsewhere and could even have been the species whose representatives had appeared among the Perimeter Worlds. If this was true, the mission of the Venturer became of even greater importance to the future of the Federation and its member worlds.

Unless the blasted world had been attacked at random the probability was that its adversary had come from somewhere in this area of the Galaxy, and the crew of the Venturer set about establishing its next destination. The nearest star ahead was Delta Canis Majoris, otherwise known as Wezen which lay more than 500 light years away. The course set, the crew reluctantly stepped into the "sleep-tanks" for the longest leg of the voyage so far.

Scarcely a single artifact had remained unscathed in the holocaust that had stripped the planet of life. Even isolated structures like this communication tower had been deliberately destroyed. Overleaf
The huge and massively built structure illustrated here was one of the few relics which was relatively intact. Obviously part of a vast industrial complex, its monolithic construction had failed to shelter any of the planet's former inhabitants from the global disaster.

CHAPTER FIVE

The warrior queen

LOG POINT: Ref. 1843. Proximity unidentified star coded VenX2.
DUTY OFFICER: ArmOff. Art West.
DRIVE MODE: Warp.
DRIVE STATUS: A1.
SYSTEMS STATUS: A1.
PERSONNEL STATUS: 7 additional passengers.

Nibor Max's innocent excursion onto the surface of the unnamed planet almost ended in disaster as a band of warlike inhabitants bore down upon him.

Time passed and the ship forged on through the parallel universe of hyperspace, its scanners and sensor equipment logging progress and monitoring the status of the sleeping crew. As the target star of Delta Canis Majoris drew nearer, the long range detection gear registered the presence of a huge cloudy mass of minute dust particles and fragments of matter. The sensors focussed on the broad interstellar mist, probing and analysing its characteristics until the shipboard computers determined that it concealed a previously unrecorded star beyond its mantle.

Although Delta Canis Majoris still lay some 180 light years further on, Dor Hewett's Intuitive Input System decided to awaken the crew prematurely. By the time they were all assembled on the main deck, the Venturer had emerged from sub-space and was hanging motionless with the small sun central in the viewscreens. The team immediately set about the standard checks and soon established that only two planets were present in the tiny system and only one was capable of supporting life. The ship eased in towards the small, dense orb as the data collectors determined albedo readings, spectrum analysis and the thousand other items of information that define a world.

Within two orbits it became obvious that the planet was inhabited, but although they spotted a large number of settlements and industrial areas, there was no sign of astro-technology. It seemed unlikely that this would prove to be the place they sought, but they decided to investigate to make sure. Selecting one of the larger artificial sites, an advance party boarded a shuttle and descended to the surface. They remained on board to await a reaction from the inhabitants who would certainly have noted their arrival.

Close by the landing site, they could see the twisted, tangled wreckage of a construction that looked distinctly like an aircraft of quite substantial size and the crew of the shuttle found it hard to contain their desire to take a closer look.

After three uneventful hours, Nibor Max decided to venture out. He made his way, under his companions' watchful gaze, towards the wreckage, then almost tumbled over a strange skeleton half-buried in the sandy soil. He picked up a mace-like object that lay beside the carcass. Suddenly, as he was examining the primitive weapon a band of mounted creatures thundered out from behind the wreck with an eerie, shrieking sound. He shouted into his intercom and one of the shuttle's particle accelerator guns boiled the ground between him and his assailants into gas. They slid to a halt in surprise, wheeled and fled into the dustpall.

Max sprinted back to the shuttle and the airlock hissed shut behind him as he threw himself onto the floor. Curious to see what would happen next, the others voted to remain on the planet, and eventually they were rewarded. Another party of the humanoids slowly and nervously came into sight, this time accompanied by a curious chariot bearing someone of obvious importance. The riders formed a line on each side of the wheeled device and the tigerish creature which drew it, and dismounting, placed their weapons on the ground. As they seemed to wish a peaceful meeting, two of the crew stepped from the shuttle, their hands extended in friendship.

After a lengthy interlude of gesture and mime, one of the warriors hesitantly agreed to be fitted with the terminals of Tik Rednop's linquistics equipment, and within an

Drawn by her interest in the armament of the shuttle, the fierce queen of a nation at war was willing only to exchange information for aid. A forced trip into orbit changed her mind, and gave her captors an important clue.

hour a basic working vocabulary had been established. The raiding party who had witnessed the Federal's display of force had returned to their base. Their report had encouraged their ''queen'', the female in the chariot, to come herself to enlist the aid of the mysterious visitors in a war that was being waged with a neighbouring nation. Although she informed them that flying craft were used widely on the planet, none, it seemed, could match the speed of the strangers' ship, or carried such fearful weapons.

Faced with the reluctance of the ''people from the sky'' to involve themselves with her struggle, she refused to answer the questions of the crew and grew increasingly restless as though wondering whether to attempt an assault on the coveted shuttle. After discussion with Mor Mikiss on the Venturer, the men in the lander decided to take the only course open to them, and while Art West knocked out the single guard with a low frequency stunner the others seized the female and blasted off to rendezvous with the ship above.

The terrifying experience of seeing her world shrink in size, while finding herself hanging among the stars, had the desired effect and she became only too anxious to assist the crew of the Venturer in any way she could.

Although the inhabitants of this isolated planet lacked a highly advanced technology, their weaponry was sophisticated enough to be capable of causing widespread destruction, as was clearly evident on the battle front.

Gently but insistently the team probed for any information that might help them in their search, and the first clues soon emerged.

The warrior queen admitted that ships of strange and awesome power that fell from high in the sky were not un-known to her. Seated beside one of the large viewports, with her world swimming in the endless night of space far below, she began to chatter into the interpreter with increasing speed and the story that began to emerge had a disquieting effect on the

figures clustered round the display screen.

The ships had arrived amid a blast of heat and flame some ten months (thirteen Earth months) earlier and had offered help and weapons in her war against the bordering nation. After the war was well under way, they had left leaving one of their number behind to give further guidance and advice. It was this being who now governed her War Council and directed their strategy from the military headquarters. In exchange for their help, the queen had agreed to allow the strangers to take over the lands of the people they were seeking to destroy, although she did not know what they wished to do there once the war was over. She had presumed the men from the Venturer were part of the race who had come

to the planet once before.

Having explained to her that they were anxious to meet the being who had been left to oversee the direction of the war, an armed party escorted her and the captured guard back into the shuttle for the return to the surface. Within minutes of landing, two riders appeared on the horizon only to disappear again in the direction of the city. The crew prepared to accompany the queen to her headquarters when a distant dust cloud warned them of the return of a much larger force, and uncertain of their reception, they decided to remain inside the craft. Moments later, the riders breasted the slope and halted and as the dust settled they parted to make way for a strange, diminutive figure mounted on a type of hover-scooter, who drifted slowly towards the lander and stopped about 50 meters in front of the exit port. There he dismounted and stood, holding his hands to the sides of his unnaturally large head as he stared at the Federal lander.

For a while there was no movement, then the "queen" pointed excitedly at the bizarre creature and indicated that this was the creature of whom she had spoken. Her voice broke the spell that seemed to have fallen over the entire scene. The crew of the lander opened the airlock and stepped out with the female and her attendant, but as soon as they emerged from the vessel, the gnome-like alien fell abruptly to his knees and grimaced in apparent agony, his hands still pressed to his head. He remained frozen into immobility until those around him began to

shift uneasily. The shuttle crew walked over and stood beside him but were unable to elicit any reaction. It was as though he had fallen into a trance. The native inhabitants, however, were becoming excited and were craning their necks and searching the sky above them.

Gradually the dark and massive shape of a huge domed craft loomed over the curve of the horizon and as it approached, four smaller jet-ships darted from its side and swept towards them. At the same time the kneeling creature rose to its feet and stood staring impassively at the shuttle's crew. While the giant ship hung motionless overhead, the smaller vessels settled amid a pall of dust, and several creatures like the one before them stepped out and approached the crew. One of them directed a scoop shaped linguistic device at the crewmen standing by the shuttle. Jancis Joh, the anthropologist, began to speak to the aliens, and after she had asked them who they were, one of them stepped in front of another of the scoops and spoke into it. The hollow, neutral voice that emerged replied that they were the Phalans and that they were the owners of this world, and asked who the crewmen were.

The team from the Venturer

Suddenly the alien figure dropped to its knees, hands pressed to its massive head in telepathic communication. Soon afterwards a huge ship appeared on the horizon from which smaller jetcraft emerged to land near the Venturer's shuttle. Contact with the mysterious Phalans had been made.

explained their presence and invited the Phalans to visit their ship. The latter agreed, and after notifying the Venturer, both groups lifted off to rendezvous with the ship above. There, after a lengthy discussion, the Phalans insisted that they escort the Venturer to their home planet in the Delta Canis Majoris system. They indicated that the Federal crew had little choice, but as the team's objective had been to track down and learn about the homeworld of the alien visitor, there seemed no reason to refuse this opportunity.

Several of the Phalans remained aboard the Venturer as the two ships set course for the distant star, but they refused to communicate any further throughout the short hyperdrive journey. Within two weeks the navicomputers shifted the Venturer into normal space mode and it hung motionless in the yellow glare of Wezen.

The linguistic device used by the aliens to communicate.

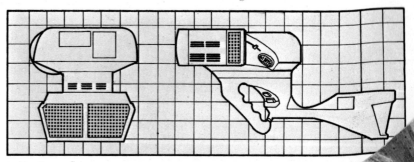

CHAPTER SIX

The Phalan empire

LOG POINT: Ref. 2215. Proximity Wezen.
DUTY OFFICER: NavOff. Richard Pontine.
DRIVE MODE: No entry.
DRIVE STATUS: No entry.
SYSTEMS STATUS: No entry.
PERSONNEL STATUS: Morale fair. All crew transferred from Venturer. Ship's Log ends.

The Federal's crew's first view of the Phalan homeworld left no doubt that they were the unwilling guests of a highly advanced species with a technology that was at least as sophisticated as that of the Galactic Federation.

As soon as they had arrived in the Wezen system, the aliens, who had until now been confined to the main deck in spite of their obvious wish to explore the Venturer, made their way to the navigational console and studied the mass chart on the display screen. After a moment, they pointed to one of the larger planetary masses shown and made it clear that this was where the Federal crew should take up an orbit. As they approached, it became apparent that this planet was the source of considerable activity, as a constant flow of craft was moving into and away from the atmosphere of the large world. To the crew of the Venturer it appeared that they had arrived at the center of a busy interplanetary trading organisation, possibly as large as the Federation itself, and certainly with the capacity to journey to the latter's Perimeter.

The computers were frantically attempting to calculate the courses of the many ships leaving the planet in order to determine their projected destinations, when the Phalans instructed them to bring the Venturer down for a surface landing. The crew protested, unwilling to bring the ship into the midst of whatever lay below, and hinted that they had no means of landing a ship of this size under gravitational conditions. To their astonishment, one of the Phalans walked directly to the Berger Gravity-Resist control board and pointed at it. Mor Mikiss shrugged and the crew took up their positions for atmospheric entry with a growing sense of foreboding as the planet, and the great industrial complexes which covered its surface, grew large in the viewscreens.

Once down, a number of small hovercars appeared beneath the hull and the entire crew was escorted to a tube-rail terminal which whisked them towards an enormous and imposing building set in the heart of the major city. There they were taken to a vast chamber whose walls were covered with charts and starmaps and which was clearly an operations center of some kind. Seated along a raised platform were twenty Phalans whose manner and bearing suggested that they were figures of some importance. The Federation team were led to individual seats, each of which was fitted with one of the scoop devices, and a force field shimmered into existence enclosing the crew in an impenetrable shell.

Then began a long and intensive interrogation as the Phalans demanded to know where the Venturer had come from, what the purpose of their journey was and whether they had been accompanied by other vessels. The team admitted only that they were the representatives of a great association of many worlds and races and had travelled alone across the vastness of galactic space to seek

A Phalan interceptor, part of their extensive weaponry.

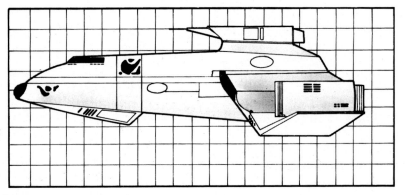

Of the scores of ships seen operating in the vicinity of the Phalan planet, most appeared to be of a distinctly military nature. It was soon clear that the crew of the Venturer were in the hands of a world at war.

origins of a strange ship that had appeared among their Perimeter Worlds. They intimated that their progress had been constantly monitored by their home base and that many Federation ships stood in readiness to come to their assistance should it prove necessary. In return they began questioning the Phalans as to the identity of the strange ship and its purpose in making the long journey alone, but were unable to elicit any response.

The Phalans appeared uncertain how they should treat the Venturer's crew and seemed to be arguing among themselves. Finally, they reached a decision. The force-field suddenly evaporated and the Federation team were led away to another chamber furnished with couches and holographic murals, where they were directed to stay. The door slid shut and the lack of any inside controls made it clear that they had little choice.

The team gathered together and discussed their predicament. One thing that seemed abundantly clear was that the Phalans were engaged in military activity of some kind. All their people carried equipment suspiciously like armaments and their dress was standardised and appeared to reflect rank. In addition, a high proportion of the ships they had seen were obviously not freighters or private craft, and

those that could have been cargo vessels were arrayed in groups which suggested that a considerable volume of supplies or material was being transported to a limited number of destinations. These facts, together with their impressions of the city as they travelled in the tube-cars across the sparsely populated, industrialised complex, led the crew to feel that they were prisoners of a race engaged in a war of substantial proportions.

The Phalans had not reacted to the Federation team's enquiry about the alien craft and their lack of curiosity implied that it was, indeed, one of their own ships. It was therefore important that its objective should be established without delay, and if it was contrary to the interests of the Federation, that Galactic Security should be informed as soon as possible. In any case, it was vital that they should be notified of the existence of the Phalans, although relaying the information to them was going to be something of a problem. Their movements were severely restricted and their ship was in the hands of the Phalans so all they could do was await further events and hope that an opportunity for escape would eventually arise. At least their captors seemed reluctant to simply destroy them.

After several hours had passed, the door again slid open, and a group of Phalans entered and gestured for them to accompany them, flanking the party as they set off down another of the smooth-walled corridors. They emerged from an airlock and found themselves standing on a small

Tubecraft hurtled the Federal team across the Phalan city to the sinister headquarters of their captors. They sensed that they had seen the Venturer for the last time.

landing apron near a thrust-engined craft towards which they were directed. They climbed aboard and were strapped into a double row of seats with their escorts. The engines fired and the craft rose with increasing speed before darting off in the direction of the city's edge. Before long, the outskirts of the city petered out to be replaced by a brief view of richly vegetated landscape before a huge spaceport filled the narrow windows. Moments later the jetcraft was descending rapidly towards one of the pads, and they bumped to a standstill.

The Phalans motioned them to step down and marched them towards a huge, silvery vessel towering above them. A boarding ramp projected from the hull and they stepped onto its moving surface to be carried inside. There they were taken to a large cabin area filled with acceleration couches and instructed to strap themselves in. A few moments later, they were thrust fiercely into the cushioning material as the massive craft shuddered and heaved them upwards. The Venturer was now further out of reach than ever and the crew suddenly felt that they had seen her for the last time. Their only consolation was that the Phalans were unlikely to be taking all this trouble in order simply to kill them. At least they could try to discover where they were being taken, and why.

CHAPTER SEVEN

The tables turn

MISSION LOG: Entry 4. Proximity Xi Puppis?
DUTY OFFICER: Commander Mor Mikiss.
PERSONNEL STATUS: Fair. Morale variable.
MISSION STATUS: Objective achieved.
Situation dangerous but contained at present.

After spending an hour in the cabin the captives were allowed onto one of the secondary decks to stretch their legs. Richard Pontine, the Navigations Officer, made for one of the viewports set into the wall and stared at the unfamiliar vista. As far as he could tell they were headed towards Wezen's nearest neighbour, a star known as Xi Puppis or Azmidiske, which was 1100 light years from Earth. Even as they watched, the view began to shimmer and dissolve into the familiar shifting colours of hyperspace. This indicated that the Phalans could make the transition while in motion whereas Federation ships had to be stationary before jumping into parallel space/time.

As far as the crew could tell, three days had elapsed by the time the ship slid into normal mode and dropped into a low orbit around a dim, bleak planet. As they drifted lower, they could see that the surface of the globe was pitted and scarred and areas of the landscape glowed with numerous fires. There seemed little doubt that they were viewing the aftermath of a devastating onslaught which reminded them of the desolate and destroyed planet they had encountered earlier in the voyage. Below them Phalan ships could be seen streaking through the atmosphere, and near the terminator, flashes and mushroom clouds showed that the battle was still in progress, and that the

Phalans themselves were the aggressors in a terrible war of attrition.

They were now hovering just above the remains of a war-torn city. A small, armoured jetcraft streaked up through the smoke and haze towards their vessel and could be heard docking in one of the lateral bays somewhere beneath them. Soon afterwards, the ship began to accelerate into the upper atmosphere and out into the darkness once again. By now, Mor Mikiss and his team knew that they should regard themselves as prisoners rather than as guests of the war-like Phalans.

All that they had seen so far indicated that the people of Wezen were pursuing a policy of expansion through military conquest and were prepared to utterly destroy any planet that opposed them. If the Federation's alien visitor had been one of their vessels it was likely that the Phalans would now regard the Federation itself as a potential adversary, and might well

A heavy Phalan attack ship of the type encountered.

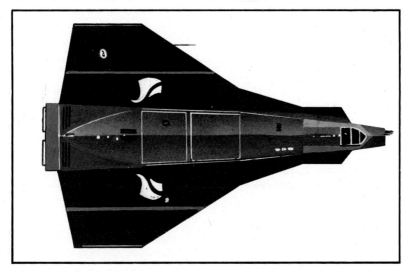

A Phalan armoured jetcraft streaked up from the surface of the war-torn planet and docked with the ship carrying the captive Federation crew. Their guides for the next stage in their journey had arrived.
Overleaf
The ship emerged from hyperspace amid an extraordinary cluster of small planets and their moons and headed for the surface of the largest body past a free-fall detector array guarding the approaches.

After flipping over, the Phalan ship slowed its descent and settled on the rocky surface. Within minutes a skimmer was carrying its passengers to a forward command base.

decide to strike before defence preparations could be made. News of this dangerous species would have to be relayed to the Security Council.

The Venturer now lay far behind them in the heart of the Phalan Empire. Their only chance was to capture another ship capable of making the voyage home. They were debating this desperate action when the view from the ports darkened as the ship emerged from warp and they found themselves in the midst of an unusual cluster of tiny planets and moons, manoeuvring for landfall. A contingent of Phalans entered the chamber and directed them back to the couches as the craft reversed its attitude and began to settle on the surface of the largest planet. A thump signalled the vessel's arrival, and as they slid off the couches their captors re-entered and led them to an exit port through which they were carried by a moving ramp to a waiting vehicle.

Once they were in their seats, the power systems whined shrilly and the armoured skimmer sped them off towards a distant collection of buildings. There they were marched along a succession of corridors to a spacious chamber deep inside the complex where their escort pushed them into a single rank before a podium and a huge viewscreen. A hush fell over the company as the screen flickered into life. The image of a great metallic head stared

impassively at them for several seconds before the neutral tones of a language synthesizer boomed from the direction of the dais. The questions, which mostly concerned the Federation's military capabilities were the same as they had been asked countless times before, and again they made no reply. Finally, the voice stopped and then spoke in the Phalan tongue to the accompanying guards.

The attitude of the guards immediately changed and they became distinctly more aggressive as they pushed the team back the way they had come. It was clear that they were about to adopt less pleasant methods to extract the information they wanted. The Federation crew would have to make their move very soon. Gambling on the absence of interpretive equipment among their escort, they whispered among themselves as the party made its way back towards the vehicle park outside. Ten Phalans were marching beside them, and the men surreptitiously edged themselves nearer to them as the group emerged from the

The Phalans' intangible leader ordered the guards to adopt more forceful interrogation techniques.

complex and headed for a small military interceptor that lay near the skimmer that had transported them to the complex.

Dick Frost, the Chief Engineer, scrutinised the ship and decided that its main drive was a fairly conventional nuclear thrust system which could be relatively easily operated provided that the controls could be identified. All that was needed was enough time for him and Dor Hewett, the Systems Officer, to study the layout and computer links. The skimmer lay just in front of them and after another whispered conference they moved into position. At a nod from Mor Mikiss they erupted into action, hurling themselves at their diminutive guards as Mor, who had been seated near the skimmer's pilot during the trip and had noted his actions, raced for the craft and Frost and Hewett sped to the sturdy interceptor.

The skimmer used in the crew's escape.

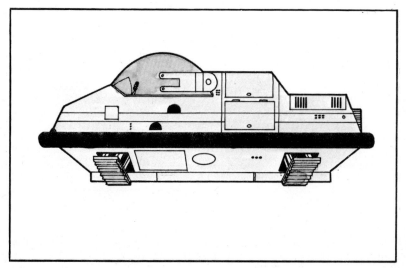

CHAPTER EIGHT

Flight to Terra

MISSION LOG: Entry 5. Proximity Xi Puppis.
DUTY OFFICER: Commander Mor Mikiss.
PERSONNEL STATUS: Good. Morale steady.
MISSION STATUS: Good. Returning with escort.

While two of his crew fled from the devastated landing apron, Mor Mikiss struggled to retain control of the captured Phalan interceptor in the desperate escape from their captors.

The guards were totally unprepared for such a dramatic change in the behaviour of their hitherto passive captives, and within seconds, all but two of them were lying unconscious or dead on the smooth surface of the landing area, with their weapons in the hands of the Federal team. Mor Mikiss, who had already leapt into the cab of the unattended skimmer, quickly checked the simple control board and set the vehicle in motion. Throwing the power rheostat to maximum, he hurled himself from the craft as it headed rapidly in the direction of the main building and the various ships parked nearby. There was a bruising shock wave followed by a deafening thump as the skimmer hurtled into the side of a small freighter and exploded violently. Flames burst from the tangled wreckage and spread to the nearest craft as a dark pall of smoke spread over the area.

Picking himself up, Mikiss sprinted to where the main party were dragging their two captives to the interceptor where the technical officers were desperately trying to isolate the guidance systems. As Dor Hewett was hastily devising basic imput and response programmes for the main control computers, Dick Frost was rigging up manual by-pass systems for the primary functions. The others clambered aboard, and the two confused and shaken Phalans were easily coerced into helping to interpret some of the specialized systems and their links to the main console. Within minutes Hewett had brought most of the computers on-line and they were able to speed up the task of tying in the controls.

One of the crew shouted a warning as scores of tiny figures began to pour out of the distant buildings and Coral Dee and Art West slipped through the exit port and dropped to the ground each clutching one of the weapons captured from the Phalan guards. Although they appeared to be a sophisticated miniaturized form of pulsed laser projector, they were easy to operate, and the two began firing at the enemy as they ran towards the far edge of the apron in an attempt to draw them off. By the time they had reached the jumble of rocky ground which fringed the perimeter, the last of the makeshift controls aboard the interceptor were keyed in and Mor Mikiss slipped behind the main console as the rest of the team secured themselves as best they could.

With a silent prayer, he set the controls and punched the interlink trigger. With a thunderous roar the nuclear line fired up and the ship lurched and lifted before gaining speed and blasting across the field. Mikiss wrestled with the controls to bring the craft round in a sweeping curve to the outcrops of rock where the two remaining crew members were entrenched, but before he was able to bring the interceptor down to ground level, a tiny craft streaked in from above and settled right beside Coral Dee and Art West. The bow section swung open and a slim figure leapt onto the ground beside them, grabbed their arms and pulled them towards the little ship. Something about the manner of the humanoid female made them enter the alien craft without hesitation, and she followed as the transparent shield swung shut.

The humanoid deftly manoeuvred the minute vessel into position alongside the cabin ports of the interceptor and gesturing for Mor Mikiss to follow her up through the atmosphere, she swiftly lifted the little craft out of sight. Mikiss struggled to keep control of the yawing interceptor as they streaked through the upper levels into the vacuum of open space. There they could see the distant gleam of

a large ship hanging in free-fall towards which the minute shuttlecraft was heading. They drew alongside the port into which it had disappeared, and a transfer tube projected from the expanse of hull and made contact with the captured interceptor's airlock. One of the Federal team slid open the inner door of the lock, hesitated and stepped into the chamber beyond to re-emerge a moment later with the news that the others were to follow as quickly as possible.

They did so and once aboard were met by Coral Dee, Art West and their female rescuer and led up to the main command deck. The ship then cast off from the empty interceptor and headed out into the darkness. Tell-tale streaks of light from the trails of Phalan pursuit ships darted up from the planet's cloud layer as the darkness shimmered and was replaced by the flickering hues of sub-space. They were safe, at least until they transferred back to the normal time/space continuum.

They turned to the slender creatures who had carried them to safety and who were now gathering around them. One of the creatures gestured to a couch which faced an impressive array of instruments and indicated that one of the humans should be seated. Recognising the instrument bank as an Interpretive Unit of some kind, Tik Rednop, the linguist, volunteered and settled himself on the resilient couch as the aliens gently positioned a net of electrodes over his head. It took almost three hours before a basic vocabulary had been established and the two

species could begin to communicate. As they spoke, a disturbing picture of the Phalans and their activities began to emerge.

The present hosts of the Venturer's crew were members of a race who had inhabited the planet they had just left. Their world had been part of a loose association of inhabited planets · which traded with each other and had, through cooperation, developed a sophisticated technology equal to that of the more distant Phalans. However, whereas they had devoted their energies to peaceful ends, the Phalans had been building up their military forces in order to seize control of the neighbouring planets and their resources.

Upon the first onslaught by the Phalans, the defenders had erected a planetary screen to protect their world from the worst effects of missile bombardment. Originally designed to ward off space hot clouds and meteor collisions, the screen needed constant repair and would eventually exhaust their shield mineral resources.

Recognising their plight, the defenders had covertly dispatched six of their ships during the early stages of the seige to head out into the Galaxy in the hope of finding a haven for the rest of their people.

It was one of these that had emerged from hyperspace among the Perimeter Worlds of the Galactic Federation. As soon as it had detected the presence of life there its crew had immediately re-entered warp for the return journey in the hope that some of their race might have survived

annihilation at the hands of the Phalan war machine.

To the beseiged defenders at home over two hundred years had passed by the time the explorer ship returned. The planetary screen had already been irreparably decimated by the Phalans. Most of the people had been destroyed in four succeeding massive attacks and the few survivors had decided to take to their ships and flee into deep space. News of the Federation Worlds arrived just in time, and even now, refugee ships were en route to the Federation in search of safety. A few ships had remained behind to look for stragglers and one of these had picked up the Venturer and monitored its course, refraining from making contact until its objectives were more certain.

They were sure now that there were no more survivors of their own race to be shepherded to safety, and offered to carry the humans back to the Federation in exchange for refuge.

The last survivors of a society overwhelmed by the Phalan onslaught provided the means of escape for the crew of the Venturer. The tiny shuttle which picked up the two crew members left on the shattered planet led them all to safety and offered them the means of returning to the Federation itself.
Overleaf
Though completely unprepared for the Phalan attack, the defenders fought with desperate ferocity for the very existence of their species. Here a Phalan warship shudders under the impact of direct hits from one of the few fighting craft opposing them.

Epilogue

The course back to the Federation was set as a wide curve in order to foil any attempt by the Phalans to plot their direction and destination. The curve ran far beyond the Galactic Perimeter before arching back into the outer edge of the spiral arm in which it lay. Although the crew of the ill-fated Venturer had aged less than a year during their epic journey, they knew that there would be little that was familiar to them on Federation planets where hundreds of years of real time had elapsed. They could only hope that whatever authority now governed the affairs of the Federation would remember who they were and what their objective had been.

It was with considerable trepidation, therefore, that the team gathered on the main deck as the ship's monitors picked up the faint signals of a Federation beacon on the furthest outskirts of the Perimeter. They watched the transitional to normal space in silence, each quiet in the knowledge that none of their old friends would still be alive and that the worlds on which they had each been born would now be as alien to them as any they had seen during the voyage into the dark unknown.

Once the transfer was completed, Mor Mikiss and Mas Rahzell, the Communications Officer, gave the commander of the refugee ship the standard Federation identification code and the signal beamed out on random broadcast; *Sender unregistered — Please supply traffic number — In-*

The course set for the return voyage carried the crew of the Venturer beyond the Galaxy in an effort to foil any Phalan attempt to track them.

ward bound for Terra — Reply code Venturer Two — Await clearance.

They transmitted continuously for almost an hour before the receivers crackled and the reply came back; *Venturer Two — You are coded UBX 9443in — Your re-entry beacon reference PC 114 — Give ETA and standby for confirmation — Please state your business and departure point — Our records incomplete.* Mor Mikiss signalled their estimated time of arrival at the Proxima Centauri beacon and explained who they were and why they would not be on the current traffic records. A little later the reply came back: *To UBX 9443in — You are cleared for inward transit Venturer Two — Welcome home.*

A Security Patrol escort and a fleet of civilian craft were waiting for them when they arrived at the beacon, and after the celebrations had ended and the team had been allowed a welcome period of relaxation and re-adjustment, the de-briefing began. There was much to tell and even more to learn over the next few weeks. The earlier refugees from the Phalan conquest had begun arriving some time ago so much of the story was already known to the authorities and contingency plans were being carried out in case the Phalans had succeeded in recording

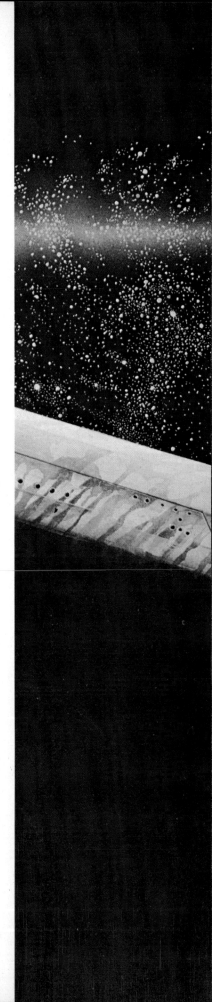

the course taken by the fleeing vessels. Most of the homeless passengers had taken the

Although the Phalans might never attempt the long journey to the Federation, defences around the Perimeter were strengthened and regularly patrolled.

opportunity to start a new life on one of the newly opened planets out on the Perimeter and the crew's rescuers were only too happy to do likewise.

After the completion of the de-briefing, some of the Venturer's crew continued in the service of the Security Force, some settled down with their

special credit ratings to civilian life and others continued work among the new colonies out on the Perimeter. Between them all, however, existed a bond forged by the knowledge that they had travelled deeper into the Galaxy than any of their fellows either had or would for a very long time.

 First English edition published 1979 by Intercontinental Book Productions, Berkshire House, Queen Street, Maidenhead, Berkshire
Copyright © MCMLXXIX by Intercontinental Book Productions
All rights reserved
This edition is published by Crescent Books, a division of Crown Publishers, Inc. by arrangement with Intercontinental Book Productions

Library of Congress Cataloging in Publication Data
Caldwell, Steven, 1947-
    Star quest.
    I. Title.
PZ4.C1478St 1979 (PR6053.A378) 823'.9'14 79-52717
ISBN 0-517-31018X

Printed in Italy